Sing Pop A Cappella

An Indispensable Guide For Unaccompanied Choirs

by Gitika Partington

Book Three

Ain't No Sunshine 6

Black Is The Colour 14

Never Gonna Give You Up 22

Rolling In The Deep 28

Sway (Quien Sera) 42

Novello Publishing Limited
part of The Music Sales Group
London / New York / Paris / Sydney / Copenhagen / Berlin / Madrid / Hong Kong / Tokyo

CW00420172

Published by
Novello Publishing Limited
14-15 Berners Street,
London W1T 3LJ, UK.

Exclusive Distributors:
Music Sales Limited
Distribution Centre, Newmarket Road,
Bury St Edmunds, Suffolk IP33 3YB, UK.
Music Sales Pty Limited
Level 4, Lisgar House,
30-32 Carrington Street,
Sydney, NSW 2000 Australia.

Order No. NOV165110
ISBN 978-1-78305-861-7

This book © 2015 Novello & Company Limited.

Unauthorised reproduction of any part of this
publication by any means including photocopying is an
infringement of copyright.

Printed in the EU.

Your Guarantee of Quality
As publishers, we strive to produce every book to the
highest commercial standards.
This book has been carefully designed to minimise awkward
page turns and to make playing from it a real pleasure.
Particular care has been given to specifying acid-free, neutral-sized paper
made from pulps which have not been elemental chlorine bleached.
This pulp is from farmed sustainable forests and was
produced with special regard for the environment.
Throughout, the printing and binding have been planned to
ensure a sturdy, attractive publication which should give years of enjoyment.
If your copy fails to meet our high standards,
please inform us and we will gladly replace it.

www.musicsales.com

Sing Pop
A Cappella

Book Three

Introduction

Some people find it hard to understand how anyone can be a musician without being able to sight-read music. Even so, I know many gifted and talented musicians who cannot read a note. There is no reason for anyone to feel insecure because they cannot read music; sight-reading is undoubtedly a skill useful at all levels of music-making, but not possessing that skill should never exclude anyone from the music-making experience. In an age when digital recorders are often available on phones, PDAs and iPods, there are always other ways of setting down music. Some people even devise their own notation system.

When it comes to transmitting music to other people who may not sight-read well or at all, the traditional practice of 'note bashing' on a piano is something with which many will be familiar. It does the job but arguably it emphasises the 'note value' of the music at the expense of conveying any feeling for, or understanding of the piece; usually these issues are intended to be addressed later.

Personally I found it a revelation when people began to teach me songs not by bashing piano notes, but by singing a line to me and getting me to sing it back several times: no notation but lots of repetition. This method makes teaching songs an option for anyone who can sing and communicate well. That in turn means many singers who do not possess the traditional qualifications of accompaniment and sight-reading skills can still take on the role of choral director. They do not even need a great voice, just an ability to sing in tune and convey the feel of the music.

As I am teaching a song, I indicate the pitch and rhythm with gestures, so adding visual information to the sound. This approach lends itself particularly well to the kinaesthetic learner who usually responds positively to being involved in some form

of physical activity and is happy to join in all aspects of this 'call-and-response' process. By contrast those who struggle most with learning songs by ear are those who have been exposed to sight-reading much too early and have consequently almost lost their auditory skills. Fortunately they too can re-learn and in my experience they often discover that it is very satisfying to be reconnected with learning by ear.

One consequence of the growth of teaching/learning by ear has been a rise in popularity of the youth choir and a cappella communities. With many singers feeling more confident about attempting to teach and lead others, the only caveat is that they must be prepared to learn all of the parts of each song themselves before attempting to teach them. One compromise is to appoint a leader per part, which can lighten the load for less experienced leaders.

Almost all my groups work on the 'Comprehensive School' ideal that by mixing very experienced singers with beginners, everyone benefits and we create a true community of singers. There is no audition policy and no requirement to be able to read music. People who have not sung for decades are sandwiched between self-assured and practised singers, and within a matter of weeks their singing and confidence improves beyond measure.

Organising singing sessions requires little in the way of premises and equipment. I like to have enough chairs for the entire group and a wall where I can Blu-Tack sheets of paper or project images from my laptop so everyone can see the words without clutching sheets. The first time I teach an arrangement, I have some form of notation with me, but in general I prefer to memorise it and teach without it as I tend to use my arms and whole body to indicate pitch rhythm and intonation.

A Little Bit on Voice Care

This is not a voice care book, however teaching a cappella can be much harder on the voice. If you are teaching alone you will be using a large range. Remember, you do not always have to sing loud since even in a big space people tend to listen carefully to quiet singing. This means you can use different qualities in your voice as you alternate between loud and soft singing.

Both male and female teachers will face some difficulties singing parts out of their natural range. I will sing bass an octave higher which to me feels as if I am singing in the same place as a bass. For a man teaching all sections of a choir I would suggest that when singing soprano and alto he sings an octave lower if it feels comfortable to do so – falsetto can be hard on the voice if you are singing for any length of time.

The Songs

This book covers some of my popular a cappella arrangements. They have all been tried and tested by singing groups of various ages and numbers. I believe that anyone who is confident that they can sing in time and in tune – and feels enthusiastic about teaching a group – should go for it. The songs range from simple to fairly challenging and I have included notes on experiences I have had when teaching them in the hope that these might prove useful to others.

I certainly don't want to discourage more traditional choirs from dipping into this book. Many of these songs and arrangements can offer a lovely contrast within a programme of classical/traditional pieces. I also believe it is desirable for a choir that spends a lot of time learning from notation to take a break and learn something by ear.

Each song in the book is covered by five tracks of audio demonstration. The first is a full performance; and the remaining four tracks each focus on one of the vocal parts (soprano, alto, tenor, bass). In these performances, the relevant part will feature more prominently, allowing the singer to learn their part more effectively. Experience shows that the practice demonstration tracks are very popular. Many choir members like to play them in the car or on iPods when commuting. They enjoy learning their parts by being immersed in the music.

Ain't No Sunshine
Bill Withers

A classic 1970s soul song. Of all the arrangements in the book this can be taught the quickest if taught well. I can teach this to any level of group in its entirety, by ear, in about half an hour. It is a real joy to sing and very effective in it's simplicity. In my experience, it works well teaching the middle "I know" sections first. This gives singers a sense of the groove of the piece without worrying about the words. The three beat gap at the end of each phrase is fun to establish (so many singers forget to stop!). This is a good section for reminding singers of the importance of watching the leader, or each other, and feeling the groove. Half-way through this section the altos have a new "I know" section which should also be taught to the tenors, as they sing it at the end of the song too. When teaching the verse, I find it a good plan to teach the bass first which is solid and on the beat, while gently singing the melody lead in between. I then teach the altos the melody, and then you can hear the 'call and response' of the soprano and bass with it. Lastly put the soprano and tenor in, these need to be gestured clearly as they come in after the bass on the off-beat of each phrase. A little extra detail is needed when teaching the sopranos the line "gone, gone too long" as they often want to swoop up and sing the bass note – sometimes finding the note they have to sing from their last line (a wholetone up) an unnatural jump.

The end section, which just layers up sections that have already been sung, can easily be extended if you have clear signals to each section of singers as to when they change their part.

Never Gonna Give You Up
Stock Aitken & Waterman

This seminal late 1980s anthem, by the magnificent Stock and Aitken, has a twist. In the chorus all parts sing what could be considered a backing vocal part that would fit beautifully over the original melody, which no one in the choir sings. It is intended here that you may invite your audience to sing the melody, as so many people know it. If you are singing this as a small group performance you may want to add the tune to the arrangement, or even some improvised phrases over the top. It is a good section to learn first because apart from the last section of the bass, all singers are singing the same rhythm.

The first introduction could be taught next with the altos split into two. This doubles as the outro as well, so you can try singing the chorus and into the outro until it flows well – a good thing to have is a well-rehearsed end section too. The second intro and verse can then be taught as another section, there are no awkward catchy bits in the verse – it is quite straightforward.

Sway
Luis Demetrio, Pablo Beltran Ruiz, English Lyrics Norman Gimbel

In the billboard charts in 1954, it was recorded by many artists including Dean Martin, Michael Bublé and The Pussycat Dolls. It started as an instrumental Mexican mambo song. It is a really fun song to sing. The rhythm in the bass is the foundation of the whole piece and less experienced singers will need to do more work on the 3-3-2 rhythm that is the bedrock for both sections of the song. We can spend time counting, but in the end the 3-3-2 has to be felt so the song can flow well. Work might have to be done with walking and gesture and repetition of a looped phrase like 'dakuta dakuta daka', to help embed the underlying feel of the song. In the second section, the tenors take over the melody on "only you have that magic technique" which should have a twinkle of fun in it.

Rolling in the Deep
Paul Epworth, Adele Adkins

This is a great number and has a real show-stopping effect as a performance piece. It can work well to start by learning chorus one and the middle section. This gives you a sense of the drama of the piece. The rhythm in the verse needs a little more work. The offbeat stabs in the tenor and bass will need singers to be really 'in the groove' – often a physical bounce. It is almost as if riding a horse on the beat, so the upbeat is felt as the moment the body is bouncing up and that can help keep the stabs tight and together. There are three chorus sections, which again, can be learned over a few sessions. Verse three has a lovely strong unison section at the beginning. Once again, you cannot under-estimate the power of some good strong unison singing. The on-the-beat stabs in the alto and soprano of the verse should be really strongly defined. This is certainly an arrangement that is well worth persevering with.

Black is the Colour
Traditional, Gitika Partington

This beautiful arrangement of an old folk song puts it into the pop ballad arena. It also gives opportunities for basses to sing some melody in verse two and three. The long smooth lines are quite repetitive and lots of help can be given when leading this piece for guiding singers from one section to another. A gesture to sig-nal the long held notes at the end of the second introduction into verse two and three can be helpful. Singers in the tenor and alto can find the drop in pitch in the repeated looped section of verse three a challenge so it is worth going over. Altos are singing quite low in their range for a while so you need to make sure they keep their tone soft and do not push their voices. Basses spend a good deal of the song singing the pedal and need to keep it light and rhythmic.

Ain't No Sunshine

Words & Music by Bill Withers
Arranged by Gitika Partington

© Copyright 1971 Interior Music Corporation.
Universal/MCA Music Limited.
All Rights Reserved. International Copyright Secured.

D.C. al Fine

8

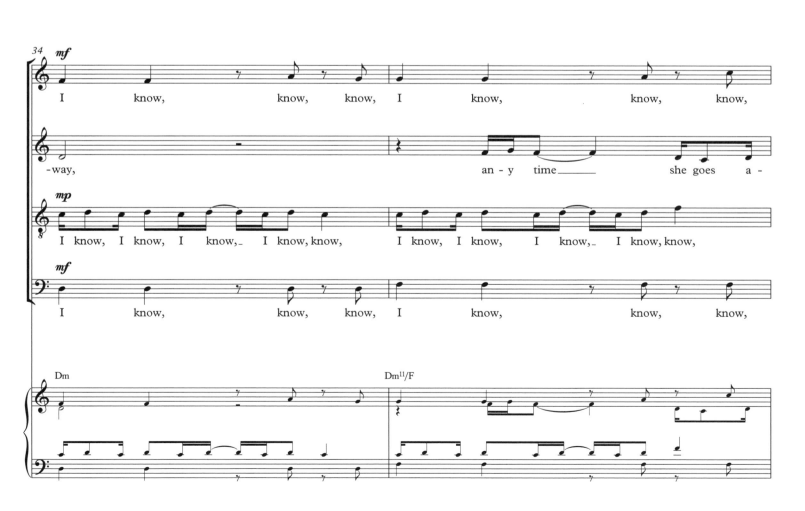

D

Black Is The Colour

Traditional
Arranged by Gitika Partington

© Copyright 2015 Novello & Co. Limited.
All Rights Reserved. International Copyright Secured.

15

ba da_ da ba da ba da_ da ba da ba da_ da

ba da_ da ba da ba da_ da ba da ba da_ da

ba da_ da ba da ba da_ da ba da ba da_ da

goes. I wish the day_ it soon_ will come when she and I_____ can be as one. I go to the

C^sus4 Cm Gm/C A♭ B♭ C^sus4 Cm Gm/C A♭ B♭ C^sus4 Cm Gm/C

I go to the Clyde_____ and I mourn and weep. Sat-is-fied, I ne'er can be.

ba da ba da_ da ba da ba da_ da

ba da ba da_ da ba da ba da_ da

Clyde_____ and I mourn and weep. Sat-is-fied, I ne'er can be. I'll write her a

A♭ B♭ C^sus4 Cm Gm/C A♭ B♭ C^sus4 Cm Gm/C

21

Never Gonna Give You Up

Words & Music by Mike Stock, Matt Aitken & Pete Waterman
Arranged by Gitika Partington

© Copyright 1987 Mike Stock Publishing Limited/Matt Aitken Music Publishing/All Boys (UK)
Sony/ATV Music Publishing (UK) Limited/Universal Music Publishing Limited/Universal Music Publishing MGB Limited
All Rights Reserved. International Copyright Secured.

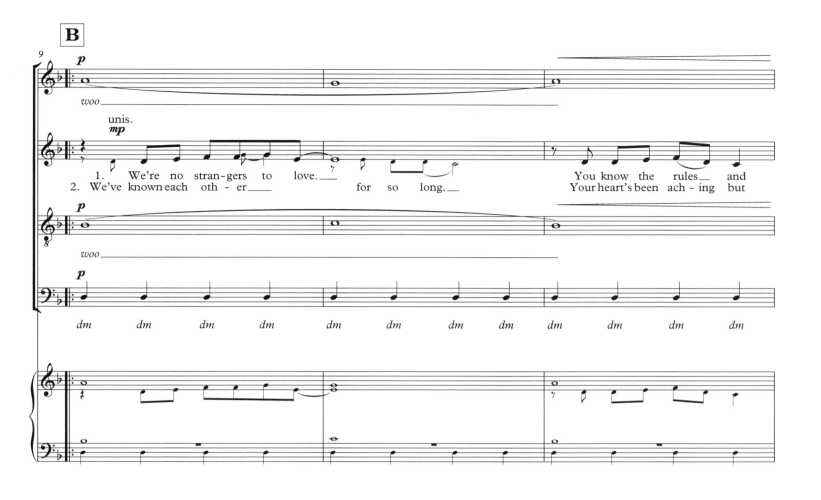

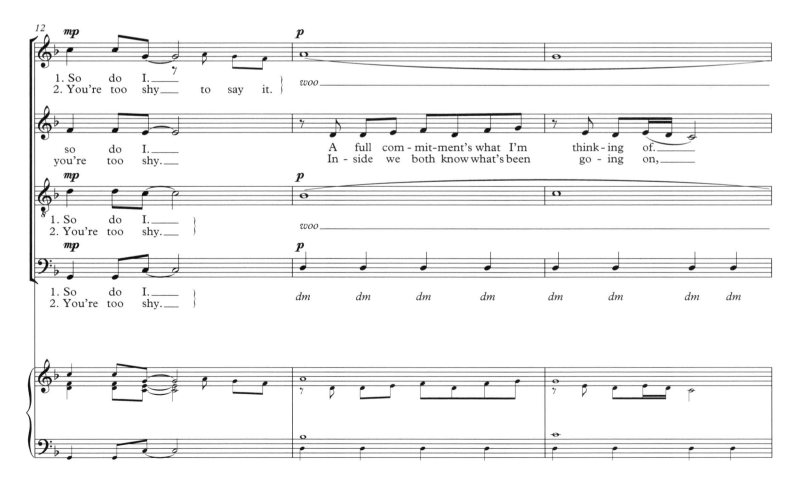

23

Rolling In The Deep

Words & Music by Paul Epworth & Adele Adkins
Arranged by Gitika Partington

© Copyright 2010, 2011 Melted Stone Publishing Ltd.
Universal Music Publishing Limited/EMI Music Publishing Limited.
All Rights Reserved. International Copyright Secured.

C

31

Think of me in the depths of your des-pair, make a home down there as mine sure won't be shared.

ba ba ba ba ba da ba ba ba ba ba ba ba ba da ba ba ba da

ba ba ba ba ba da ba ba ba ba ba ba ba ba da ba ba ba da

Think of me in the depths of your des-pair, make a home down there as mine sure won't be shared.

The scars of your love re-mind me of us, they keep me think-ing that we al-most had it

oo

oo

oo

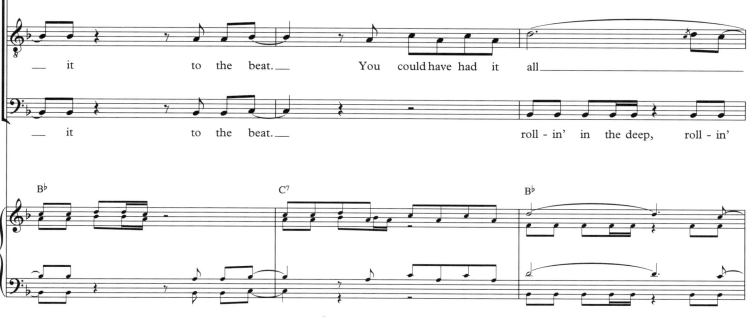

You had my heart in - side_____ your hand____ and you played __ it to the beat. ___

You had my heart in - side your hand____ and you played __ it to the beat. _____

You had my heart in - side your hand____ and you played __ it to the beat. ___ We could have had it

in the deep, oh____ roll- in'in the deep, roll- in' in the deep, and you played __ it to the beat. ___ We could have had it

C   Dm   C   B♭

You're gon-na wish you nev- er had met me, tears are gon-na fall, roll-ing in the deep.

You're gon-na wish you nev- er had met me, tears are gon-na fall, roll-ing in the deep.

all_____ roll-ing in the deep._____ You had my heart in-

dum ba dum ba dumbadumba dum ba dumba dum, dum badum ba dumbadumba dum badumba dum

Dm   C   B♭

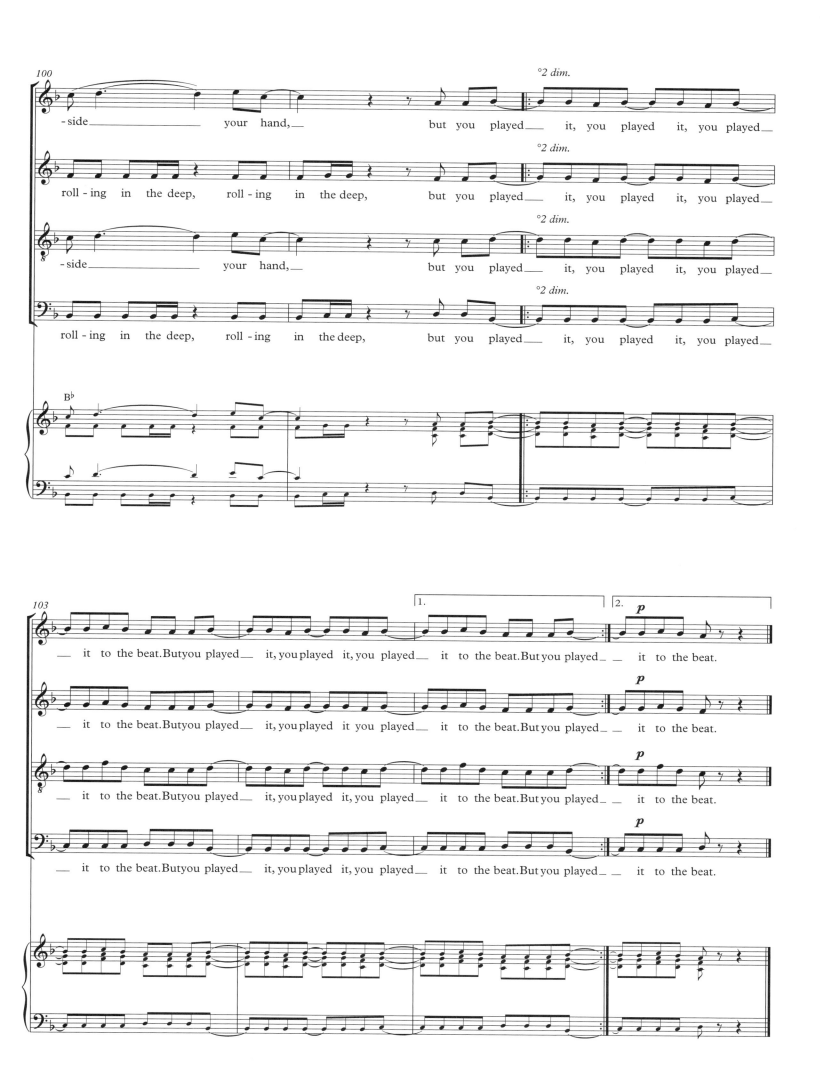

41

Sway

(Quien Sera)

Words & Music by Pablo Beltran Ruiz & Luis Demetrio Traconis Molina

English Lyrics by Norman Gimbel

Arranged by Gitika Partington

© Copyright 1953 Editorial Mexicana de Musica International SA.
Latin-American Music Publishing Company Limited.
All Rights Reserved. International Copyright Secured.

123456789

Audio Demonstration Track Listing

1-5
Ain't No Sunshine
Withers
Universal/MCA Music Limited.

6-10
Black Is The Colour Of My True Love's Hair
Traditional
Dorsey Brothers Music Limited.

11-16
Never Gonna Give You Up
Stock, Aitken, Waterman
Sony/ATV Music Publishing (UK) Limited/
Universal Music Publishing Limited/
Universal Music Publishing MGB Limited

17-21
Rolling In The Deep
Epworth, Adkins
Universal Music Publishing Limited/EMI Music Publishing Limited.

22-26
Sway (Quien Sera)
Beltran Ruiz, Traconis Molina, Gimbel
Peermusic (UK) Limited.

HOW TO DOWNLOAD YOUR MUSIC TRACKS

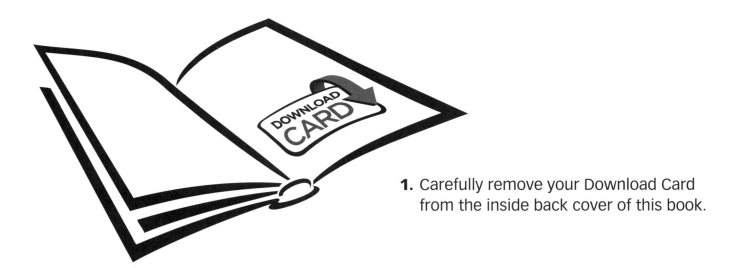

1. Carefully remove your Download Card from the inside back cover of this book.

TO REDEEM THIS CARD VISIT
www.musicsalesdownloads.com

ENTER ACCESS CODE:

XXXXXXXXX

Download Cards are powered by Dropcards.
User must accept terms at dropcards.com/terms
which are adopted by The Music Sales Group.
Not reedemable for cash. Void where prohibited or restricted by law.

DCARD1006478

2. On the back of the card is your unique access code. Enter this at www.musicsalesdownloads.com

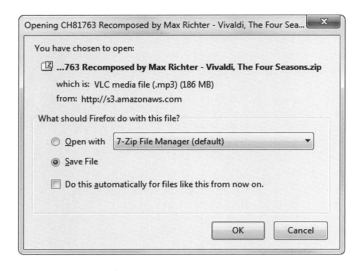

Opening CH81763 Recomposed by Max Richter - Vivaldi, The Four Sea...

You have chosen to open:

...763 Recomposed by Max Richter - Vivaldi, The Four Seasons.zip

which is: VLC media file (.mp3) (186 MB)

from: http://s3.amazonaws.com

What should Firefox do with this file?

◯ Open with 7-Zip File Manager (default) ▼

◉ Save File

☐ Do this automatically for files like this from now on.

OK   Cancel

3. Follow the instructions to save your files to your computer*. That's it!

*Appearance of download manager will vary depending upon operating system and web browser.
In case of difficulty when downloading files, please contact dropcards.com/help
Card missing? Please contact music@musicsales.co.uk